This book belongs to

....

This is the story of Three Billy Goats Gruff.

You can read it yourself – it's not very tough.

Why not give it a try, if you're brave enough?

One thing more – can you guess what?

On every page there's a worm to spot!

Three Billy Goats Gruff

Illustrations by Katie Saunders

make
believe
ideas

Three goats live in a grassy valley. They are called Little Will, Brother Bill, and Rough Tough Gruff.

A nasty troll lives under
the bridge. He is called Sid.
He likes to eat goats.

One day, Little Will wants
to cross the bridge to the
other side of the valley.

Little Will runs to the bridge.
Sid the troll jumps out and
sings . . .

"I don't want chicken,
or beef, or pork.
I want some goat
on my fork!"

Keep off

"Don't eat me," says Little Will. "Wait for my brother. He will give you some Goat Surprise."

"Goat Surprise?" says Sid.
"That sounds yummy!"

Next, Brother Bill comes along. Sid the troll jumps out and sings . . .

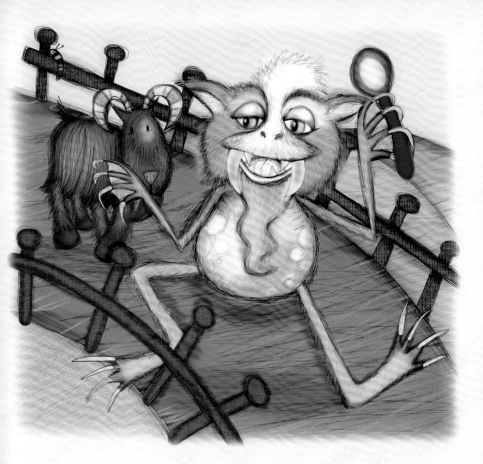

"I don't want plums,
or grapes, or prunes.
I want some goat
on my spoon!"

"Don't eat me!" says Brother
Bill. "Wait for my brother.
He will give you some
Goat Surprise."

"Goat Surprise?" says Sid.
"That sounds great!"
"All you have to do is
wait," says Brother Bill.

Rough Tough Gruff
runs onto the bridge.
Sid the troll jumps
out and sings . . .

"I don't want carrots,
or beans, or peas!
I want some goat
on my plate, please!"

Rough Tough Gruff says,
"Pick on someone your
own size! Here's my
special Goat Surprise!"

Rough Tough Gruff
charges at Sid and
gives him a kick.
Sid feels sick.

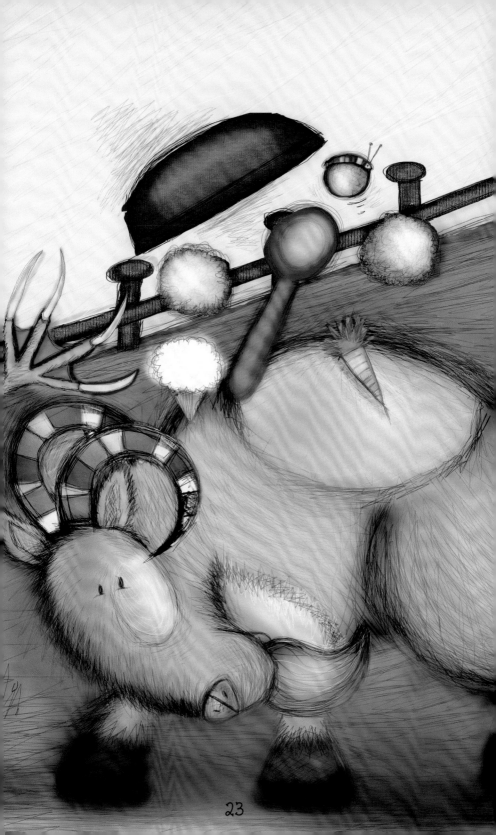

The goats live happily in the grassy valley. Sid the Troll moves far away.

Do not enter

Ready to tell

Oh no! Some of the pictures from this story have gotten mixed up! Can you retell the story and point to each picture in the correct order?

Picture dictionary

Encourage your child to read these words from the story and gradually develop his or her basic vocabulary.

bridge

carrot

goat

grass

kick

plate

troll

valley

worm

Key words

Here are some key words used in context. Help your child to use other words from the border in simple sentences.

The goats **like** grass.

Bill stands **on** the bridge.

Sid has **big** teeth.

"Goat is **my** favorite dinner!"

Gruff charges **at** him.

Grow a grassy meadow

The three billy goats wanted to get up to the good grass on the green meadow. Here's how to grow a beautiful "meadow" that you can enjoy eating.

You will need
- a new face cloth, or about ten sheets of paper towel
- a large plate or plastic tray • mustard and cress seeds
- scissors • a spoon

What to do
1 Put the face cloth or paper towel in a pile on the plate or tray. Soak the cloth or paper by spooning cold water onto it.

2 Sprinkle mustard and cress seeds over the damp cloth or paper.

2 Put the plate or tray on a sunny windowsill.

4 Sprinkle with water each day so the paper doesn't dry out. At the same time you can see if your seeds are starting to sprout shoots.

5 After a few days your "meadow" will be covered in green mustard and cress "grass" that's ready to harvest. Use the scissors to cut off as much as you need. Mustard and cress taste very good in egg salad sandwiches. You could probably even eat it with roast goat – but don't tell Sid the Troll!